THE HAPPY BODY

Journal

ALSO BY ANIELA AND JERZY GREGOREK

Non-Fiction
The Happy Body (2009)
I Got This: The Art of Getting Grit (2016)
Self Mastery Workbook (2017)
The Happy Body Virtues (2019)

Poetry
Sacred and Scared (2014)
Food for Your Soul (2014)
Locket: A Mother in the World (2016)
Family Tree (2018)

Dialogues
The Happy Body: Mastering Food Choices (2015)
The Happy Body: Mastering Exercise Choices (2015)
The Happy Body: Mastering Rest Choices (2015)

Translations
Late Confession by Józef Baran (1997)
Watermarks by Bogusław Żurakowski (2000)
Her Miniature by Zbigniew Czuchajowski (2000)
In a Flash by Józef Baran (2000)
The Poetry of Maurycy Szymel (2004)
The Shy Hand of a Jew by Maurycy (Mosze) Szymel (2013)
Native Foreigners: Jewish–Polish Poetry Between the World Wars (2015)

CD
Food for Your Soul (2013)

Videos
The Happy Body Ambience (2013)
The Happy Body Exercise Program (2014)

THE HAPPY BODY

Journal

by
Aniela & Jerzy Gregorek

The Happy Body Press
Woodside, California
2019

Please direct inquiries to:

The Happy Body Press
104 Alta Mesa Rd.
Woodside, CA 94062
E-mail: thbp@thehappybody.com

ISBN 978-1-7330441-1-0

First Edition

The Happy Body Journal
by Aniela & Jerzy Gregorek

Cover photo: Depositphotos.com

Cover and text design by Alexander Atkins Design, Inc.
Manufactured and printed in the US, on acid-free paper.